W9-BZD-803

**15 Minutes a Day**

First Grade Success

# Reading and Writing

For information about permission to reproduce selections from this book for
an entire school or school district, please contact permissions@highlights.com.

Published by Highlights Learning • 815 Church Street • Honesdale, Pennsylvania 18431
ISBN: 978-1-64472-536-8
Mfg. 07/2020
Printed in Madison, WI, USA
First edition
10 9 8 7 6 5 4 3 2 1

For assistance in the preparation of this book, the editors would like to thank:
Vanessa Maldonado, MSEd; MS Literacy Ed. K–12; Reading/LA Consultant Cert.; K–5 Literacy Instructional Coach
Jump Start Press, Inc.

# When They Grow Up

A joey becomes a kangaroo.

A tadpole becomes a frog.

A fawn becomes a deer.

An acorn becomes a big oak tree.

And pumpkin seeds will grow to be...

pumpkins!

Reading Comprehension: Informational Text: Photo Essay

Read the text. Answer the questions.

1. What is the main idea?
   - ○ Living things grow up.
   - ○ Living things have different names.
   - ○ Animals and plants are living things.

2. Which is a kind of seed?
   - ○ acorn
   - ○ frog
   - ○ joey

3. How are tadpoles and fawns alike?
   - ○ Both live in water.
   - ○ Both are adult plants.
   - ○ Both are young animals.

4. Draw a line to match each young animal to its parent.

# Babies and Parents

Draw pictures that show a young animal and a parent. Below each picture, write to complete the sentence frame.

Title: _____

Written by: _____

A _____

becomes a _____.

A _____

becomes a _____.

Writing: Informational Text: Picture Essay

Pictures can give extra information.

A _____

becomes a _____.

A _____

becomes a _____.

Can you find 5 differences between these 2 pictures?

5

# Adventures of Spot

"Time to clean up," says Pa.

Spot and Pa work hard.

Pa finds his hammer.

Spot finds his ball.

Time to play!

Read the story. Then answer the questions.

Characters are people or animals in a story. The setting is where a story takes place.

I. Who are the characters?

○ Pa, Ma    ○ Pa, Spot    ○ Ma, Spot

2. What is the setting?

○ a food store     ○ a tool shed     ○ a school

3. What happens in the story?

○ Spot and Pa clean up and then play.
○ Spot and Pa make dinner.
○ Spot and Pa build a doghouse.

Write **I**, **2**, and **3** to put the pictures in order.

# Tell a Pet Tale

Draw pictures that tell a story about a pet. Below each picture, write to tell what happens.

Title: _____

Written by: _____

_____

_____

_____

_____

_____

Writing: Narrative: Picture Story

Pictures can show story characters and events.

Two of these rabbits look exactly alike. Can you find the matching pair?

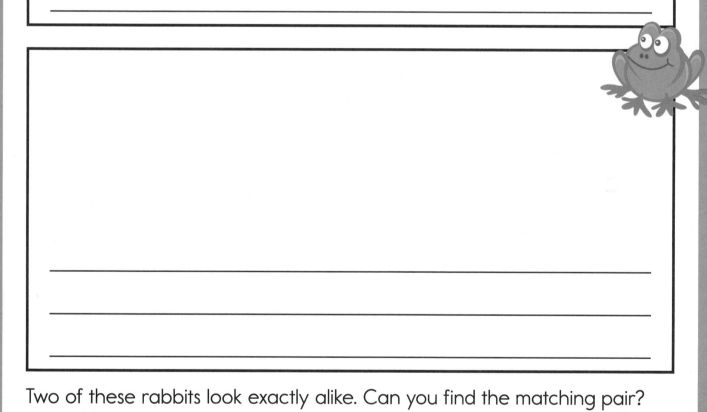

# A Story of Evergreens:

Winter was close. It was time for birds to fly away. But one bird hurt his wing. He could not fly. He sat in a maple tree.

A folktale is a story that has been passed down by storytellers.

"Go away!" said the tree. "It is time for my winter nap."

The oak tree said, "Go away!"

"Hide in my branches," said a pine tree.

"Eat my berries," said a holly tree.

Then Old Frost said, "It is time to start winter."

"I will blow leaves off the trees," said the wind.

"What about the trees that helped the bird?" said Old Frost.

"They have been kind," said the wind. "They may keep their leaves all winter."

# A Korean Folktale

Read the folktale. Answer the questions.

1. What do many birds do when winter is close?

_____

2. Why didn't the little bird go with the other birds?

_____

_____

3. Why did the wind let the pine and holly trees keep their leaves?

_____

_____

4. Do you think this is a true story? Why or why not?

_____

_____

Circle the trees that helped the little bird. Draw a rectangle around the trees that did not help.

MAPLE    OAK    PINE    HOLLY

# Word for Word

Read each underlined word. Write the **2** words from the word box that have almost the same meaning. How are the words different?

> branches   broken   glared   hurt   jumped
> leaped   looked   small   tiny   twigs

1. One bird had <u>injured</u> his wing.

_____   _____

2. He <u>hopped</u> onto a maple tree.

_____   _____

3. The tree <u>stared</u> at the bird.

_____   _____

4. "Go away, <u>little</u> bird!"

_____   _____

5. "You can snuggle in my low <u>limbs</u>."

_____   _____

Circle the strongest word in each sentence.

Today is (cold/freezing/cool).

We (slide/skate/glide) on the ice.

She (zooms/rides/moves) down the hill on her sled.

He (flies/soars/lifts) into the air.

That moose is (huge/big/gigantic)!

Our day was (great/amazing/good)!

What silly things do you see?

13

# My Folktale

Think up a folktale of your own. Your story might tell how the giraffe got its long neck. Then complete the story map.

Characters

Setting

Beginning

Middle

End

Write your folktale using the characters and ideas in your story map.

Title: _____

Written by: _____

_____

_____

_____

_____

_____

_____

_____

_____

_____

_____

# L A T E
## 1  2  3  4

Use the number code above to solve this riddle.
**What is a giraffe's favorite type of bedtime story?**

Answer: ____  ____  ____  ____  ____  ____  ____  ____  ____
      2      3     2     1     1     3     2     1     4

# Meet the Luna Moth

The luna moth is a kind of insect. It has spots on its wings. The spots look like the moon. *Luna* means *moon*. The spots look a bit like eyes, too. The "eyes" scare away animals that try to catch it.

Informational text **gives facts that can be proven.**

A luna moth grows inside a cocoon. Then it comes out. Its wings are soft and small. They grow wider and harder. The moth can get as big as a man's hand! It is one of the biggest moths.

A luna moth lives up to 10 days. It sips from flowers. But it does not eat. It ate food as a caterpillar. It lives on that food.

Look for luna moths at night. That is when they fly.

Read the informational text. Use the facts from the story to answer the questions.

1. The luna moth is:

   ○ a reptile      ○ an insect      ○ a bat

2. *Luna* means:

   ○ sun      ○ one      ○ moon

3. The spots on a luna moth's wings can look like:

   ○ eyes      ○ a man's hand      ○ a butterfly

4. These wing spots might scare off:

   ○ a plant      ○ an animal      ○ a man

5. You might see luna moths:

   ○ in the morning      ○ at lunchtime      ○ at night

Draw a line between each insect and its match.

# The Life of a Butterfly

Look at each underlined word. Use the context clues—the words and pictures that surround it—to find the meaning.

1. A butterfly <u>hatches</u> from a tiny egg.
   - ○ comes out of an egg   ○ flies
   - ○ crawls

2. A newly hatched butterfly caterpillar is called a <u>larva</u>.
   - ○ melted rock  ○ young insect  ○ moon

3. When the caterpillar is big, it forms a <u>chrysalis</u> around itself.
   - ○ leaf       ○ a hard skin       ○ wing

4. At last an insect <u>emerges</u> from its chrysalis.
   - ○ sleeps   ○ eats   ○ comes out into view

5. It has <u>transformed</u> from a caterpillar into a butterfly!
   - ○ changed       ○ grown       ○ fixed

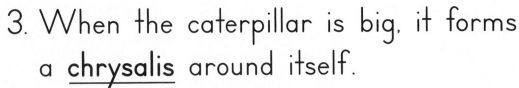

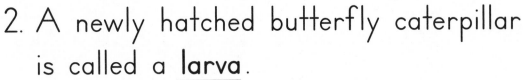

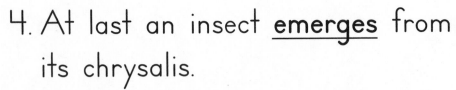

# Butterfly House

Use the context clues to fill in each sentence with a word from the word box.

> crowded  exclaim  observe  squirms  startled

Our class is visiting an indoor garden. It is
_____ with more than 60 different kinds
of butterflies!

Sam is _____ when one lands on his nose.

I look down and _____, "One is on
my finger!"

Another one _____
out of its chrysalis.

Ravi uses his magnifying
glass to _____ it.

How many butterflies do you see?

# Go Buggy!

Get ready to write an informational paragraph about a bug. Complete this text map. Look up facts if you need to.

An informational paragraph gives facts about a topic.

**Topic sentence:**

My favorite bug is _____.

**Detail 1:**
What does it look like?

_____

_____

_____

_____

_____

_____

**Detail 2:**
What does it eat?

_____

_____

_____

_____

_____

_____

**Detail 3:**
Where does it live?

_____

_____

_____

_____

_____

_____

**Closing sentence:**

I like this bug because _____

_____.

Write an informational paragraph. Follow your text map.

_____

_____

_____

_____

_____

_____

_____

_____

_____

_____

Use veggies and cream cheese to make bug-shaped snacks!

# A Kite-Flying Day

Indi, Tex, and Niko were at the park with Niko's mom. They wanted to fly their kites.

Tex said, "If we hold our kites high, maybe the wind will catch them." But that didn't work.

"Maybe we should run really fast like this," said Indi. But that didn't work either.

"I think this may not be the best kite-flying day," said Niko's mom. "We might need to try again on a windier day."

As they headed for home, a strong gust of wind came along. It sent Tex's kite up, up, up! Niko and Indi saw Tex's kite flying high, so they quickly tried again.

"Look!" said Niko. "My kite is flying, too!"

"And so is mine!" said Indi.

"Hooray," cheered Niko's mom. "I guess it was the perfect kite-flying day after all."

Read the realistic story. Then answer the questions.

1. Where does the story take place?

_____

2. What problem do Indi, Tex, and Niko have at the beginning of the story?

_____

_____

3. What does Indi suggest they try?

_____

_____

4. What finally makes the kites fly?

_____

_____

What differences do you see between these two pictures?

# Pin Down a Problem

Pin up your ideas for a realistic story. Complete this story map.

A good story has a problem and characters who try to solve the problem.

Characters

_____

_____

_____

Setting

_____

_____

_____

Problem: What is wrong?

_____

_____

_____

Solution: How do the characters try to solve the problem?

_____

_____

_____

Write a realistic story. Follow your story map.

Title: _____

Written by: _____

_____

_____

_____

_____

_____

_____

**Help Lily solve her problem! Can you find her 12 missing lemons?**

_____

_____

_____

_____

_____

_____

_____

# Penguin Cup Cozy

A cup cozy keeps drinks hot and protects fingers. Here is how to make one.

## You Need
- scissors  • black sock
- paper cup  • white and orange felt
- black marker  • glue

A how-to gives step-by-step directions.

1. With an adult's permission, cut off the foot part of a **black sock**. Pull the top part of the sock over a **paper cup**.

2. Cut **white felt** in the shape of a penguin face. Use a **black marker** to draw on eyes.

3. Cut a triangle from **orange felt**. **Glue** the triangle to the face.

4. Glue the face to the sock. Let it dry.

Read the directions and look at the pictures for making a Penguin Cup Cozy. Then write the answers to the questions.

1. What things do you need to make the cup cozy?

_____

_____

_____

2. What do you do with the top of the sock?

_____

_____

_____

3. How do the pictures help you make a shape like a penguin face for Step 2?

_____

_____

_____

4. What is the last step you need to do to finish the cozy?

_____

_____

_____

# Step by Step

Write your ideas on how to "build" your favorite craft or your favorite sandwich.

## Project

How to _____

You need

_____  _____  _____

_____  _____  _____

### Step 1

_____

_____

### Step 2

_____

_____

### Step 3

_____

_____

### Step 4

_____

_____

Writing: Informational Text: Steps in a Process

Write your how-to. Follow the ideas you wrote.

Title: _____

Written by: _____

_____

_____

_____

_____

_____

_____

_____

Help the construction worker meet his friends for lunch. Draw a clear path from START to FINISH.

START

FINISH

# The Dog and the Bone

A dog trotted down a path. She had a big bone in her mouth. Then she came to a stream. She looked in the water. There she saw another dog! It had a bigger bone. Yum! That bone looked good.

A fable is a story that teaches a lesson.

"Give me that bone!" she growled.

But the other dog did not let go. It held on to its bone.

She opened her mouth to bark. This made her drop her bone. Splash! It fell in the water. It sank out of sight.

The other dog and its bone disappeared, too!

Sadly, the dog trotted home. Now she had no bone at all.

Read the fable. Then answer the questions.

1. How was the dog feeling at the start of the fable?

_____

2. What did the dog see as she crossed the stream?

_____

3. Why did she growl?

_____

4. How did the dog feel at the end of the story?

_____

_____

_____

_____

These dogs have hidden their bones. How many can you find?

5. What lesson did you learn from this fable?

_____

_____

_____

# Fable Fun

Think up a fable of your own. Your lesson might be "Slow and steady wins the race" or "Be careful what you wish for." Complete this story map.

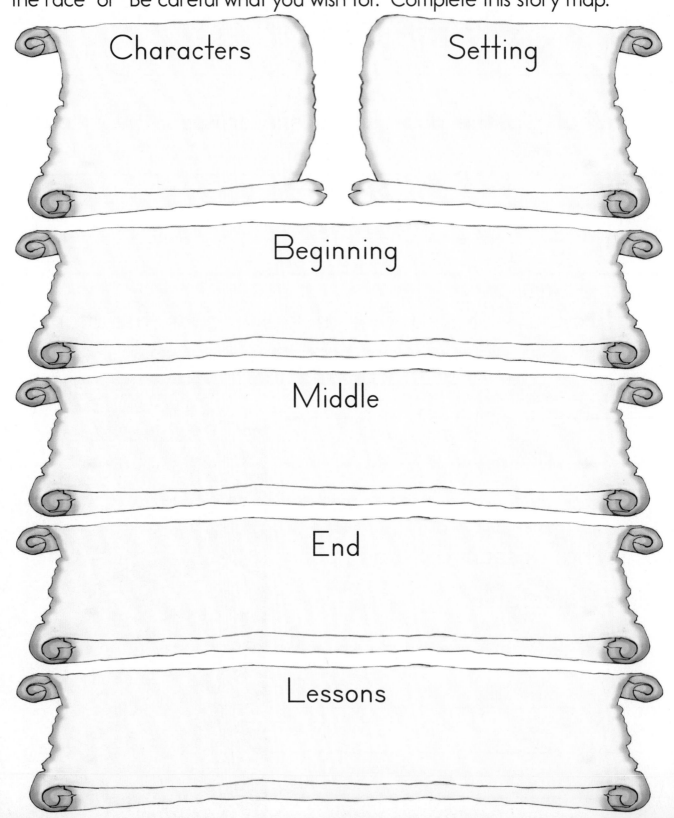

Characters

Setting

Beginning

Middle

End

Lessons

Write your fable from the notes on your story map.

Title: _____

Written by: _____

_____

_____

_____

_____

_____

_____

_____

_____

_____

_____

_____

# Tortoise or Turtle?

Most tortoises live on dry land. A tortoise has sharp claws. Claws help it dig a hole. It spends most of its time in this hole. That way, it stays out of the hot sun. It comes out to eat plants. It gets water from plants as well as food. A tortoise moves slowly. It hides in its shell if hungry animals come near. Some tortoises live to be more than 100 years old!

Compare to tell how things are alike. Contrast to tell how they are different.

Most turtles live near water. A turtle spends most of its time in the water. It has webbed feet to help it swim. Some turtles have flippers. A turtle can hide in its shell. Turtles can live up to 70 years. Turtles eat plants. Turtles also eat meat. They may eat bugs and fish. They may even eat hamburger!

Draw a line from each fact to the correct animal.

Eats plants

Eats meat          ○

Has webbed feet

TURTLE

Lives in dry places

Lives in wet places          ○

Hides in its shell

BOTH

Can live up to
100 years

          ○

Can live up to
70 years

TORTOISE

# Sort It Out

Read the story. Look for words that belong in the same group. Write them in the correct column below.

The boy in the green shirt had a vanilla sundae. The man in the white shorts had mint ice cream in a cone. The clerk made a strawberry shake for a woman wearing a pink hat. Ava dripped chocolate on her new yellow shoes!

| Colors | Clothing | Flavors |
|--------|----------|---------|
| _____ | _____ | _____ |
| _____ | _____ | _____ |
| _____ | _____ | _____ |
| _____ | _____ | _____ |

Find and circle the **5** objects in this Hidden Pictures puzzle.

cane     scissors     fork     envelope     flashlight

Write words to describe each animal. Use words from the word bank and other words for color and size.

bird   cat   flies   fur   jumps   large
legs   small   spots   stripes   swims   tail

Duck

_____

_____

Tiger

_____

_____

Zebra

_____

_____

Panda

_____

_____

# Good Sports

Compare and contrast basketball and tennis. Use the pictures below. Write words in the Venn diagram to organize your thoughts.

| Basketball | Both | Tennis |
|------------|------|--------|
| _____ | _____ | _____ |
| _____ | _____ | _____ |
| _____ | _____ | _____ |
| _____ | _____ | _____ |
| _____ | _____ | _____ |
| _____ | _____ | _____ |
| _____ | _____ | _____ |
| _____ | _____ | _____ |

**Basketball**

**Tennis**

Write a paragraph that compares and contrasts basketball and tennis.
Use ideas from your Venn diagram.

_____

_____

_____

_____

_____

_____

_____

_____

_____

_____

_____

_____

_____

_____

# A City Rap

As I'm walking down the street,
I click my fingers to the beat.
Car horns beep and tires skid;
I hit the top of a metal lid.

Babies cry, a cell phone rings;
I tap my feet to the sound of things.
Children shout in a noisy crowd;
I hum the rhythm and laugh out loud.

Litter crinkles, puddles plop;
I knock the wall—I cannot stop.
As I am walking down the street,
I click my fingers to the beat.

A poem uses words to make a reader feel a certain way or to paint pictures in a reader's mind.

Read the poem. Then answer the questions.

1. How does the boy feel as he is walking?

   ○ sad            ○ happy            ○ angry

2. Write a word from the poem that rhymes with *crowd*.

   _____

   _____

3. What sounds does the boy hear?

   _____

   _____

4. What things does the poem help you see?

   _____

   _____

5. How does this poem make you feel? Which words in the poem make you feel that way?

   _____

   _____

# Spelling Feelings

Read the story below. Circle each word that describes a feeling.

Tom was tired. It was the day of the spelling bee. He had worked hard to get ready. His friend Pam said she felt happy. But Tom was worried. What if he made a big mistake? He was also a bit sad. His grandma lived too far away to come. He wished she could be there.

Then his name was called. Tom felt shaky when he got his first word to spell. But soon he was happy. He was able to spell "shaky"!

Later, Tom missed a word. He did not win the bee. He felt sad. But his parents were still proud of him. Even better, he saw Grandma! She had made it to the bee!

# This Makes Sense!

Use your 5 senses! Write the words from the word box that best fit each sense column. Some words might fit more than I sense. But write each word only once.

Some words tell how things look, smell, sound, feel, or taste.

bright  creaky  crunchy
dark  fluffy  fresh  heavy  juicy  quiet
rotten  scary  sharp  sour  squeaky  stinky

It looks
_____ _____ _____

It smells
_____ _____ _____

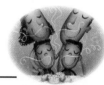

It sounds
_____ _____ _____

It feels
_____ _____ _____

It tastes
_____ _____ _____

Now read the poem on page 40 again. Circle the words that describe sounds.

# Read All About It

A book report gives the book's title, author, characters, and the main idea of the story. It gives an opinion by the reader and reasons for that opinion.

Read this book report. Underline the title, then circle the author's name. Underline the reader's opinion, then circle the reasons for that opinion.

An **opinion** is what a person thinks about something. A **reason** tells why the person thinks a certain way.

My favorite book is *Mossy* by Jan Brett. It is about a turtle who grows plants on her shell. My favorite part is when she starts to grow a garden on her shell. I love this book because I love turtles and plants.

Can you say this tongue twister five times fast?

**BENNY BETTA BUYS A BOOK.**

# My Favorite Book

Write a book report about your favorite book.

**15 Minutes a Day**

**Highlights**

# Congratulations!

(your name)

worked hard
and finished

First Grade Success

## Reading
## and Writing

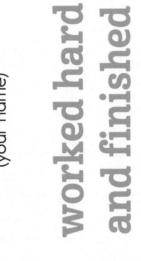

# Answers

## Page 3
### When They Grow Up
Which is a kind of seed?
acorn

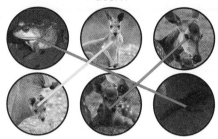

## Page 5
### Babies and Parents

## Page 7
### Adventures of Spot
1. Who are the characters?  Pa, Spot
2. What is the setting?  a tool shed
3. What happens in the story?
Spot and Pa clean up and then play.

③ ① ②

## Page 9
### Tell a Pet Tale

## Page 11
### A Korean Folktale

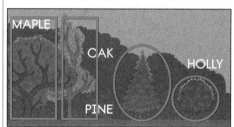

MAPLE
OAK
HOLLY
PINE

## Page 12
### Word for Word
One bird had injured his wing.
broken hurt

He hopped onto a maple tree.
jumped leaped

The tree stared at the bird.
looked glared

"Go away, little bird!"
small tiny

"You can snuggle in my low limbs."
twigs branches

## Page 13
### Word for Word
Today is (cold/freezing/cool).

We (slide/skate/glide) on the ice.

She (zooms/rides/moves) down the hill on her sled.

He (flies/soars/lifts) into the air.

That moose is (huge/big/gigantic)!

Our day was (great/amazing/good)!

## Page 15
### My Folktale
What is a giraffe's favorite type of bedtime story?

A TALL TALE

## Page 17
### Meet the Luna Moth

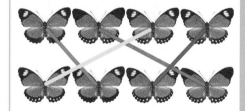

## Page 17
### Meet the Luna Moth
1. The luna moth is: an insect
2. *Luna* means: moon
3. The spots on a luna moth's wings can look like: eyes
4. These wing spots might scare off: an animal
5. You might see luna moths: at night

## Page 18
### The Life of a Butterfly
1. A butterfly **hatches** from a tiny egg. comes out of an egg
2. A newly hatched butterfly caterpillar is called a **larva**. young insect
3. When the caterpillar is big, it forms a **chrysalis** around itself. a hard skin
4. At last an insect **emerges** from its chrysalis. comes out into view
5. It has **transformed** from a caterpillar into a butterfly! changed

## Page 19
### Butterfly House
Our class is visiting an indoor garden. It is crowded with more than 60 different kinds of butterflies!

Sam is startled when one lands on his nose.

I look down and exclaim, "One is on my finger!"

Another one squirms out of its chrysalis.

Ravi uses his magnifying glass to observe it.

# Answers

### Page 19
### Butterfly House

8 BUTTERFLIES

### Page 23
### A Kite Flying Day

### Page 25
### Pin Down a Problem

### Page 27
### Penguin Cup Cozy

1. You need scissors, a black sock, a paper cup, white and orange felt, a black marker and glue.

2. Pull the top part of the sock over a paper cup.

3. You can use the picture at the bottom to see how face is shaped.

4. Glue the face to the sock. Let it dry.

### Page 29
### Step by Step

### Page 31
### The Dog and the Bone

### Page 31
### The Dog and the Bone

1. How was the dog feeling at the start of the fable?  Happy she had a bone.

2 What did the dog see as she crossed the stream?  Another dog.

3. Why did she growl?  The dog had a bigger bone.

4 How did the dog feel at the end of the story?  Sad she had no bone.

5. What lesson did you learn from this fable?  Jealousy doesn't pay.

### Page 35
### Tortoise or Turtle?

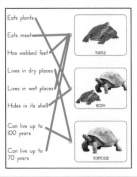

### Page 36
### Sort It Out

| Colors | Clothing | Flavors |
|---|---|---|
| GREEN | SHIRT | VANILLA |
| WHITE | SHORTS | MINT |
| PINK | HAT | STRAWBERRY |
| YELLOW | SHOES | CHOCOLATE |

### Page 41
### A City Rap

1. How does the boy feel as he is walking?  happy

2. Write a word from the poem that rhymes with crowd.  loud

3. What sounds does the boy hear?  car horns beep, tires skid, babies cry, cell phone rings, children shout, litter crinkles, puddles plop

4. What things does the poem help you see?  the city neighborhood

### Page 42
### Spelling Feelings

Tom was tired. It was the day of the spelling bee. He had worked hard to get ready. His friend Pam said she felt happy. But Tom was worried. What if he made a big mistake? He was also a bit sad. His grandma lived too far to come. He wished she could be there.

Then his name was called. Tom felt shaky when he got his first word to spell. But soon he was happy. He was able to spell "shaky"!

Later, Tom missed a word. He did not win the bee. He felt sad. But his parents were still proud of him. Even better, he saw Grandma! She had made it to the bee!